M000032492

AS YOU WANNA BE

A Collection of Fun, Thought-provoking
Questions for the 1990 - 2000's

By

Deborah A. Williams

Syan Books

Publisher's Cataloging-in-Publication Data

Williams, Deborah A.

Black as you wanna be.
1. Afro-Americans. 2. Afro-Americans--Social life and customs. 3. Black culture. I. Title.

GN 365.4 W478   1991   305.8'96'073   91-67334

ISBN 0-9631151-3-8

Library of Congress Catalog Card Number: 91-67334

Cover design and graphic layout - Arthur Hedges

SYAN BOOKS
P.O. Box 90168
Pasadena, California 91103

Manufactured in the United States of America
First Edition - 1991

10 9 8 7 6 5 4 3 2

DEDICATION

To my loving, supportive, and brilliant husband -
the counselor ~

And to my parents, the most loving and giving
parents in the world ~

ACKNOWLEDGEMENTS

Special thanks to my family, Leslie Hedges and Amber Hedges, for their infinite counsel and for being an eternal source of inspiration. I thank Arthur "Pancho" Hedges for his many hours of artistic and graphic assistance. My thanks to Eric Yeldell for his legal guidance and encouragement. To Cheryl Williams, Dustin Johnson, and Emery Johnson for their ardent assistance, and who are always there for me. I thank Karen Patterson for her editorial advice and input. And for their continued support, I thank Dimmy Young Hedges, Barbara Augustus, Aubrey Williams, and Alvah Jalila Larsuel.

And thanks to my special crew "in effect," Shawna Williams, Derrell Higgins, Marcius Glass, Shawn Fondal, and Corey Campbell for their assistance in test marketing and focus group research around the college set - you guys are winners!

INTRODUCTION

Black As You Wanna Be contains two-hundred of the most thought-provoking and controversial questions for today's thinking and aware person. This intriguing collection of probing, stimulating questions explores many issues that are uniquely experienced and understood by African-Americans today.

Black As You Wanna Be takes a fun approach to examining some of the current and important issues in today's society, like teenage pregnancy, Black-on-Black crime, drugs, inter- and intra-racial problems, education, Black pride and values. This book promotes essential discussions and conversation of these issues, as well as other interesting and light-hearted issues - then allows the participants to reach their own insightful conclusions and solutions.

There are no right answers to these questions - or perhaps there are - but only you can determine what is right.

Read this book with your loved ones, your spouse, your old friends, your new friends, your homeboys and homegirls, co-workers, etc. You're guaranteed an exciting and memorable experience!

One Final Note: The contents of this book are HIGHLY FLAMMABLE when mixed with honesty, emotions, facts, and opinions. If an explosion is eminent, close the book and take cover!

HOW TO READ
Black As You Wanna Be

When reading the questions, you might follow the format described here. Each question is numbered. When playing with a group, one person can act as the moderator or reader. Each person in the group can take a turn and call out a number, and then answer that particular question.

Or you could start at the beginning of the book with question one, and proceed through question two-hundred.

Or the reader might choose a particular question for the person responding.

However you choose to play, get ready for a fun, entertaining time that you and your friends will certainly remember!

BLACK
AS YOU WANNA BE

1

Would you object if one of your family members married a Caucasian person?

2

Would you sacrifice 15 years off your life if it would end apartheid and civil strife, and establish successful Black rule in South Africa?

3

Would you date someone who wears a jeri curl?

4

Have you ever had a sexual relationship with someone outside your race? If not, would you have the desire to?

5

If you received a fully-paid scholarship to attend a top-rated, prestigious, predominately White university, or to attend one of the renowned and famed Black colleges, which would you choose?

6

You have been dating someone for two months. Would you have sexual intercourse with that person without using a condom?

7

If you were isolated in a large, empty chamber for one month, what three things would you take with you?

8

During a physical exam, your doctor (of the opposite sex) starts making sexual advances toward you. What would you do?

9

If you could spend the day with any one person, who would it be?

10

You are at a small social party, engaging in a casual conversation with several new acquaintances. One woman, with a noticeably long hair weave, is expressing her opinions on the importance of African-American pride and consciousness. Do you find a contradiction with her hair style and her opinions? If so, do you point it out to her?

11

Have you ever had a lustful fantasy about a stranger you've seen?

12

If you found out that your best friend was addicted to and selling crack cocaine, what would you do? (Would you consider turning him into the authorities?)

13

If your spouse divorced you, and married someone who was almost half your age, would you be angry and resent them for it?

14

Which do you think is the worst: being lazy; being selfish; or procrastinating?

15

If you were stranded alone on a desert island for two months, then rescued, which would you want:
- as much of your favorite foods as you wanted; or
- all the sex you wanted with the person of your dreams?

16

What would you do with your winnings if you won a $1 million dollar lottery?

17

What quality or accomplishment are you most proud of in yourself?

18

If you are watching a game show on TV, and there is an African-American contestant, do you cheer for him and hope he will win?

19

Would you want to live to be 150 years old?

20

You find out that the reverend of your church is gay. Would you have a problem with it?

21

Do you think that African-American police officers are as quick to commit police brutality as their Caucasian counterparts?

22

Would you be upset if your soon-to-be spouse invited an ex-girlfriend or ex-boyfriend to your wedding?

23

Would you tell your mate if one of his or her close friends made sexual advances toward you?

24

Your brother has contracted AIDS. He needs care and has lost his home. Would you let him move in with you?

25

Do you believe that light-skinned African-Americans secretly harbor feelings of contentment that they are not dark-skinned?

26

An elderly couple is kissing passionately in public. Do you think their behavior is shameful?

27

You are consistently late for social affairs that you and your good friend attend together. Your good friend has told you that if you are late one more time, he will leave without you. This time, you are late - and he leaves you behind. Would you get upset with your friend?

28

If you could cheat on an exam without getting caught, would you?

29

───◇◇◇◇◇───

You are married, but physically attracted to someone you work with. That person continually flirts with you, and decides one day to warmly embrace you and caress you in private areas. Do you allow this to happen?

30

Your 15-year-old niece has become pregnant. Do you recommend that she goes through with the pregnancy and raises the child; puts the child up for adoption; or has an abortion?

31

Would you date someone you work with?
Why or why not?

32

Your friend has borrowed $300 dollars from you, and promised to pay you back as soon as possible. She has not yet paid you, but tells you about a beautiful, new coat she just bought and an expensive dinner at a fancy restaurant. What, if anything, do you say to her?

33

Would it bother you if an African-American comedian performed jokes that were excessively derogatory towards African-American people? What about if a Caucasian comedian performed those jokes?

34

Do you have any regrets in life? If so, what are they?

35

If you could move to Kenya and be rich beyond your wildest dreams - but could not return to the United States for 25 years, would you do so?

36

You find out that your spouse is having an affair. Do you divorce him or her?

37

Do you think that most African-American men would prefer a woman with long, flowing, straight hair?

38

Do you think that most Caucasian women believe that African-American men are "blessed" with large genitals?

39

If you and your mate were having problems with your sex life, would you consider seeing a professional sex therapist or counselor?

40

You work for a large, successful Fortune 500 corporation, and have a chance to be promoted to manager of your division. You are in the process of planning a small party at your home. Do you invite your boss and other Caucasian division managers who must recommend and approve your promotion?

41

Do you think there are enough positive African-American role models for children? Do you think the media gives them enough exposure?

42

If you had a choice between watching either a championship boxing match or a championship tennis match, which one would you watch?

43

Would you be embarrassed to go into a video store and rent an X-rated video?

44

Which is more important to you when choosing a mate: attractive looks; having money; or intelligence?

45

What age do you think is appropriate to begin having sexual intercourse? What age, if any, to stop?

46

Is rap music a true art form that is here to stay?

47

If you could choose to be Caucasian, would you? How about for one week?

48

What person do you most admire - living or dead?

49

In the year 2050, do you think there will be more or fewer interracial couples and marriages?

50

Do you think that using the word, "nigger," to refer to others is ever appropriate?

51

If you had $1 million dollars that could be spent on either ending hunger in African nations or on pleasure cruises, an expensive home and cars for you, which would you choose? You could not divide up the money.

52

An unfriendly Asian grocer in the Black community continually refuses to allow more than three African-American students into his store at one time. Do you oppose or agree with his policy?

53

Do you believe that poverty breeds crime?

54

―――――

You go to the bank and withdraw $1,000 dollars in cash. When leaving, you wait for the elevator down to the parking lot. As the elevator door opens, five young Black men who look "street tough" are in it. Do you enter the elevator and ride it down? If it was a group of street-wise White young men, would you enter?

55

A friend you work with has asked you to write her a letter of recommendation for a new job. You are not confident in this person's ability to do a good job or competence. What do you do?

56

Would you marry someone of a different race than yourself?

57

Do you believe that more parental intervention, better education, or some other strategies would help to reduce teenage pregnancies?

58

Would you shoot an intruder who came into your home?

59

You survive a tragic accident, but are rendered helpless; you are in a vegetative, non-functioning, invalid state, and cannot feed, bathe, or dress yourself. Would you want your life support equipment shut off? There is no chance of full recovery.

60

Would you marry someone who was currently in or had served time in prison?

61

Would you put your aging parents in a nursing home if you could afford it?

62

If you witnessed gang members committing a brutal murder, would you testify against them in court?

63

Do you think there will be, in your lifetime, or ever, social and economic equality for all in America?

64

Do you prefer to be identified as "Black," "African-American," or would you prefer some other multi-cultural ethnic term that defines a mixed heritage? Do these numerous labels erode the unity of Black people?

65

In the next political race for governor of your state, two qualified candidates are running. One is an African-American, and the other is a Caucasian. Which candidate would you vote for?

66

Are there many hypocrites in your church congregation?

67

Who is your favorite athlete?

68

If you had a choice of being either extremely rich or extremely beautiful or handsome, which would you choose?

69

Describe the ideal place to have sex.

70

Do you think that using "glow-in-the-dark" or bright, rainbow-colored condoms would be fun?

71

If your lover has bad breath, do you tell him or her about it?

72

Would you visit a psychic?

73

Do you think that "date rape" by someone you know, is any less of an offense than rape by a stranger?

74

If your best friend decided that he or she now preferred to date only White people, would that change your feelings about your friend?

75

Do you think that criminals who commit "Black-on-Black" crime are worse than other types of criminals?

76

Your best friend had recently dated a person for a brief time. They are no longer dating, and now that person wants to date you. Would you go out with him or her?

77

Do you worry about getting older?

78

When you see an interracial couple together, does it bother you? Why or why not?

79

Do you think that older people are treated with enough respect in this country?

80

Would you consider joining the Nation of Islam and becoming a Black Muslim? (-if you are not already a member-)

81

Do you believe that the man should be the head of the household?

82

Your mother has been viciously raped and murdered. The criminal gets off on a technicality. There is absolute, positive proof that this is the correct rapist and murderer. Would you pay someone to kill this vicious criminal?

83

If you could wish for any one thing, what would it be?

84

Would you object to your 14-year-old son having his ear pierced?

85

If you could choose either to immediately lose 10 pounds or receive $100 dollars, which would you choose?

86

Do you think that an older person who dresses very youthfully looks silly?

87

Do you prefer to have an African-American, a Caucasian, or other doctor and dentist? Does it matter if your doctor and dentist are male or female?

88

Whom do you think is the most attractive
African-American actor or actress today?

89

Do you think it makes a significant difference if children have a single-parent home
or a two-parent home?

90

Do you ever feel self-conscious about eating watermelon when you are in a group of Caucasians?

91

Would you go to a nude beach? If so, would you go nude? Would it make a difference if you were in a foreign country?

92

~~~

You are in a mall, and there is a group of
African-American kids being boisterous,
talking and laughing excessively loud,
and making a "scene." Are you embarrassed by their actions?

93

If you had only three months to live, what would you want to do with the rest of your time?

94

If you found $50,000 dollars in cash, would you keep the money or turn it in?

95

Do you believe that if you achieve success in your career and life, you should give something back to the community, and help other African-Americans?

96

Do you think that violence, other than in self-defense, is ever justified?

97

If your child was mixed with African-American and Caucasian heritage, would you raise him with African-American pride and culture, or with Caucasian pride and values?

98

If you worked in a small office with four other people, and one of them had offensive body odor, would you tell that person?

99

Do you think that most African-Americans over thirty viewed Malcolm X as too militant?

100

If you found out that your neighbor practiced voodoo, juju, or witchcraft, and she invited you over for dinner, would you go?

101

If you divorced your spouse, would you ever re-marry the same person again?

102

Do you think that African-Americans should patronize Black-owned businesses and professionals, for greater economic development?

103

If your potential spouse was very wealthy, and refused to marry you unless you signed a pre-marital or pre-nuptial contract, would you sign it?

104

If hypertension ran in your family, would you continue to eat pork?

105

Have you ever faked an orgasm?

106

If you had been married to the same person for 17 years, and your sex life had become boring, what would you do to liven it up?

107

Would you ever use a dating, match-making service?

108

Have you ever done something that made you feel like an "Uncle Tom"? What about in a job situation?

109

Would you find it difficult to talk about sex
with your children? With your parents?

110

Do you think that hair weaves, relaxers, curls, hot combing, fade creams, and colored contact lenses, are all a form of deep-seated Black self-hatred?

111

If you were at a friend's house, and he told you to look in the closet for something - and you spotted a life-sized inflatable doll, would you think that he was strange?

112

Do you believe that oral sex is immoral? If not, do you believe that if it is performed on you, that you are obliged to reciprocate?

113

Do you believe that gay couples should be allowed to marry each other?

114

You and your spouse have been arguing constantly, and have been unhappy for the last year. You recently had a new baby. Do you stay together for the child, or break up?

115

Would you be jealous if your mate flirted with others?

116

Do you think that most politicians are honorable or corrupt? What about most lawyers?

117

Are you honest with your mate?

118

Do you think that women should not curse or use foul language? What about men?

119

If you were offered $50,000 to pose completely nude for a magazine, would you do so? What about $200,000?

120

If your mate gave you a venereal disease, would you leave her or him?

121

Did you vote in the last major election? If not, do you feel guilty about it?

122

Would you continue to belong to your church if the reverend was caught having an affair with one of the church members?

123

Do you think that too many television shows and movies portray African-Americans in negative or undesirable roles and images, like in crime, drugs, prostitution, poverty, and slavery? What themes or subjects would you like to see film-makers depict in the media?

124

Is education the way to improve conditions in and a way to get out of the ghettos and the projects?

125

If one of your children had treated you horribly, and with no respect throughout the years, would you leave them out of your will?

126

Do you think that female news reporters should be allowed in the locker room immediately after a professional sporting event?

127

If the company you work for did not celebrate the Martin Luther King holiday, would you do so anyway, and not report to work?

128

If you had a choice of moving and remaining for the next 10 years of your life to either Paris, France or to Lagos, Nigeria, which would you choose?

129

<svg>decorative divider</svg>

You are currently dating two potential spouses. One is a doctor who is not physically attractive. The other is a shoe repair clerk with an exceptionally gorgeous face and body. All other things being equal, which one would you choose to marry?

130

Do you think that Caucasian couples should be able to adopt African-American children?

131

What quality do you value most in your mate?

132

If you could save the life of a member of the White Aryans, or the Skin Heads, or the Ku Klux Klan, would you do so?

133

Do you think that the schools that specialize in teaching and instilling values exclusively in young African-American males are good?

134

Do you think that Black children can learn more from a good Black teacher than from a good White teacher?

135

Do you think there is something wrong with the American justice and socioeconomic systems, if the overwhelming majority of the U.S. prison population is African-American and Hispanic? Is there anything we can do to help alleviate or remedy this situation?

136

It is 2:00 a.m., and you are driving home from a party. On the side of the road, a woman, who appears to be alone, is trying to flag you down - with her car lights flashing and hood up. Would you stop to see if you could assist the woman?

137

Do you think that drug pushers or dope dealers are any worse than drug users? Are they both morally wrong?

138

If your child's teacher posed nude in a magazine, would you still want that teacher to teach your child?

139

What animal do you most resemble?

140

Are Affirmative Action employment goals or minority hiring quotas fair?

141

Have you ever lied on a job interview?

142

Do you have a problem with a man staying at home to raise the children, while the woman goes out to work?

143

Your 18-year-old daughter does not get along with her new step-parent. They continually bicker and have heated arguments. The step-parent wants you to put the 18-year-old out of the house. What would you do?

144

Are you ever envious or jealous of others?

145

Do you think that lyrics in music that promote sexually exploiting and abusing women, and promote racism should be censored?

146

In the year 2090, how do you think African-American people will differ from today?

147

Do you think that cigarette and alcohol ads that are targeted specifically to African-Americans should be banned?

148

When African-American children use "Black English" or slang, should they be taught otherwise?

149

Do you think that a young African-American man should go on a job interview with dread locks or designs shaved into his hair? Do you think his hairstyle would affect his ability to get the job?

150

If your mate asked you to wear the skimpiest lingerie or G-string, and perform a dance for him or her, would you do so?

151

Do you ever "kiss-and-tell," or have you ever discussed the intimate details of one of your romances with a friend?

152

Do you think that young adults who are unable to read should be allowed to graduate from high school?

153

Do you think that all schools should acknowledge and celebrate Kwanzaa as well as Christmas?

154

Would you run a red traffic light at 2:00 a.m. if you had been waiting for two minutes, and it still had not changed to green?

155

If a close friend told you that ghosts appeared at her house, danced around, and stroked her body, would you believe your friend?

156

If you found out that a friend had sexually molested his child, and had committed incest, would you continue to be friends with that person?

157

If a person had become pregnant as a result of being raped, or a victim of incest, would abortion be acceptable for that person?

158

Your new mother-in-law comes for a one-week visit to your home. She is a smoker, and you do not permit smoking in your home. Do you ask her to smoke outside?

159

If you were a vice president in a top-ranking, Fortune 500 company, would you feel an obligation to talk with and interview other African-Americans who were seeking employment with your firm?

160

You are 42 years old. Would you consider having a romantic relationship with a 21 year old?

161

What does your mate think your worst fault is? What do you think it is?

162

How do you rate yourself on a scale from one to ten, with ten being the best?

163

Describe an incident in your life that caused you extreme embarrassment.

164

Do you think that drugs and/or prostitution should be legalized?

165

What would you do if someone of the same sex flirted and made a pass at you?

166

If you were 35 years old, and wanted to get married and have children, but had not yet found a suitable mate, would you lower your standards?

167

Could you marry someone without feeling passion for her or him?

168

Are you a vain person?

169

Do you believe in astrology and horo-scopes?

170

You find out that one of your best friends is bisexual. Would it seriously affect your friendship?

171

Do you think it is a good policy to omit or spare the truth if it is going to deeply hurt someone?

172

Does your mate nag you, complain, and demand too much?

173

Do you think there is anything wrong with a busy executive having his or her secretary get them coffee and run personal errands?

174

If your mate physically abused you, would you stay in the relationship?

175

If you saw your good friend's spouse having an affair with another person, would you tell your friend about it?

176

Do you know any compulsive liars?

177

If you saw your 7-year-old child masturbating, would you stop him or her?

178

Would you allow your 19-year-old son or daughter to have sexual intercourse in your home?

179

Would you be too jealous to marry someone in the limelight like a pro basketball player, an actress, or a popular musician?

180

If you were a doctor, would you treat and operate on AIDS patients? Would you treat others with serious, contagious illnesses?

181

Do you think it is alright for a child to be raised by a gay couple?

182

Dr. Martin Luther King, Jr. and Malcolm X were two of our leaders and heros from the past. Today, many of our heros are local community leaders. Who, in your opinion, are our leaders of today?

183

Your mate insists that if he or she cooks, then you should wash the dishes, and vice versa. Do you agree with this arrangement and uphold your end of the bargain?

184

Would you prefer to have a woman or a man for a boss?

185

In 1988 the median income of African-American families was only 58% of White families, and almost 44% of all African-American children lived below the poverty line. Are better education and better government policies enough to remedy this situation?

186

If your wealthy parents died without leaving a will to divide up their estate, and you had three other siblings, would you fight over the estate?

187

You and your spouse have been married for five years, and have been trying, unsuccessfully, for those five years to have a baby. Would you consider using a surrogate mother?

188

Would you be embarrassed to see a psychiatrist?

189

If the manufacturer of one of your favorite products practiced racial discrimination, would you join in a boycott against the product?

190

⬥⬥⬥⬥⬥⬥⬥

Do you think that people who practice
group sex and wife-swapping are immoral? Why or why not?

191

It is the Christmas season. And you are a landlord with tenants that have not paid their rent for three months. Would you evict them one week before Christmas? They have two small children.

192

Have you ever watched a topless dancer or attended a male exotic dancer show? If yes, have you ever given them money or a tip?

193

Do you believe that you can catch the AIDS virus from french-kissing?

194

If you were getting a massage, and the person giving you the massage touched you in one of your private areas, and told you it was part of the massage, what would you do?

195

Would you like to have a male secretary?

196

Do you think that most men "worship" large breasts?

197

Do you think there will be, in your lifetime, an African-American President or Vice-President of the United States?

198

If you frequently had highly exciting, erotic dreams or fantasies that did not include your mate, would you feel guilty?

199

If you were hiring for a job opening, and a white South Afrikan applied for the position, would you hire him?

200

Do you know anyone who sometimes passes for Caucasian?

Photo By Haywood Galbreath

ABOUT THE AUTHOR

Examining and questioning complex issues has always been a passion of Deborah Williams, especially since she graduated with a B.A. in Philosophy/Psychology from the University of California - Irvine.

And as a Black woman and mother, particularly, analyzing the current and future status of Black people is a critical concern for Ms. Williams. The current state of affairs of African-Americans; the introspective state of our Blackness, culture and values; and what the future holds for our children, are all vital issues for the author.

Ms. Williams has traveled extensively throughout the United States, and has been fully exposed to the North and the South. She has also been integrally involved in corporate America. These observations and experiences are reflected in her writing.

Ms. Williams also holds a Master's Degree in Business Administration from the University of Southern California. With over ten years of marketing management experience, she has been responsible for developing some of the most innovative and successful marketing and promotion campaigns in the industrial products industry. Ms. Williams has written extensively in the corporate marketing field.

Postscript: Through writing this book, other essential questions have evolved for the author, including:

~ Are our culture and values flourishing?
~ Are we operating with a healthy mind-set?
~ Where will we be in the 21st Century?
and
~ Will our children encounter a thriving and just world in the future?

It is Ms. Williams' hope and goal to provide readers with a forum to begin to determine these answers and trends for our future.